Other books by Exley:
Horse Quotations
Horses a Celebration

Published simultaneously in 1994 by Exley
Publications in Great Britain, and Exley Giftbooks in
the USA.

ISBN 1-85015-517-8.

Pictures selected by Helen Exley.
Designed by The Pinpoint Design Company.
Picture research by P. A. Goldberg and J. Clift/Image
Select, London.
Typesetting by Delta, Watford, U.K.
Printed and bound in Hungary.

**Exley Publications Ltd, 16 Chalk Hill, Watford,
Herts WD1 4BN, UK.
Exley Giftbooks, 232 Madison Avenue, Suite 1206,
New York, NY 10016, USA.**

Cover: THE WATERING PLACE
HAROLD HARVEY (1874-1941)
Bonhams, London
The Bridgeman Art Library

Title page: GOING TO PASTURE
DOROTHY ADAMSON, D. 1934
Townley Hall Art Gallery & Museum, Burnley
The Bridgeman Art Library

• *The Beauty of* •
HORSES
A D D R E S S   B O O K

EXLEY
NEW YORK • WATFORD, UK

A

God forbid that I should go to any heaven where there are no horses.
R.B. CUNNINGHAM-GRAHAM

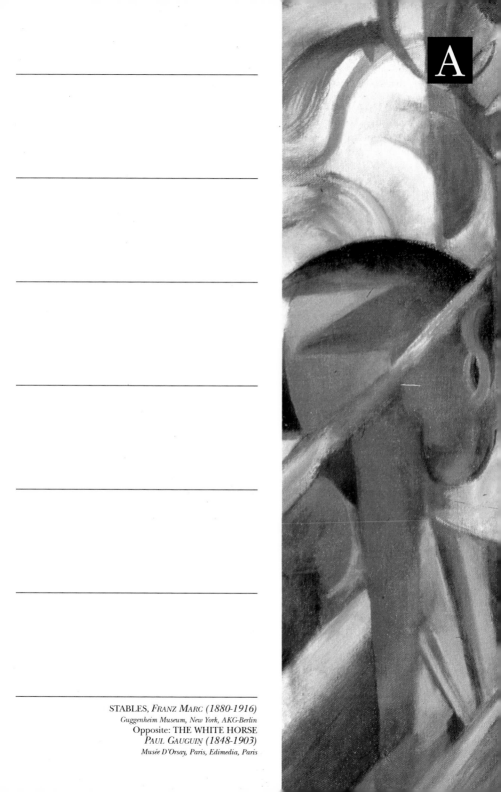

B

No whisper of lover, no trilling of bird,
Can stir me as hooves of the horses have stirred.
WILL H. OGILVIE

B

FREEDOM, *YVONNE DELVO*,
Private Collection, Bridgeman Art Library
Opposite: SPRING FEVER, *ROCKWELL KENT (1882-1971)*
Pushkin Museum, Moscow, Bridgeman Art Library

B

The rhythm of the ride carried them on and on, and she knew that the horse was as eager as she, as much in love with the speed and air and freedom.
GEORGESS MCHARGUE

C

A RIDE ON THE BEACH, DUBLIN
HEYWOOD HARDY (1843-1933)
Julian Simon Fine Art, London, Bridgeman Art Library
Opposite: HERMIT LEADING HORSES TO DRINK
MORITZ VON SCHWIND, Schack-Galerie, Munich, AKG-Berlin

C

We dominate a horse by mind over matter.
We could never do it by brute strength.
Monica Dickens, b. 1915

C

ELENA AND MARIA IN TRADITIONAL
VALENCIAN COSTUME, *SOROLLA Y BASTIDA JOAQUIN
(1863-1923), Museo d'Arte Moderna, Barcelona, Scala*
Opposite: THE GRASS FIRE, *REMINGTON VON FREDERIC
(1861-1909), Amon Carter Museum, Fort Worth, Texas, AKG-Berlin*

D

A good horse and a good rider are only so in mutual trust.
H.M.E.

D

HORSEMEN ON THE ROSE COLOURED BEACH
PAUL GAUGUIN (1848-1903)
Folkwane Museum, Essen, AKG-Berlin
Opposite: WHITE HORSE, *GIOVANNI FATTORI (1825-1908)*
Gallery of Modern Art, Florence, Scala

E

*...the horse has been, of all animals, man's most
constant companion in work and leisure.*
FROM "HORSES"

E

THE ROAD TO THE HOUSE
Carlo Balestrini (1868-1922), Private collection, Edimedia, Paris
Opposite: PARISIAN QUAY
Gotthardt Kuehl (1850-1915)
Neue Meister Art Gallery, Dresden, © Erich Lessing, AKG-Berlin

F

The delicate and exquisite horse is itself a work of art.
BERTRAND LECLAIR

F

GROOM AND MARE, *PATRICK HENNESSY*
Taylor Gallery, London, Bridgeman Art Library
Opposite: THE FOALS, *JULIUS PAUL JUNGHANS (1876-1953)*
Josef Mensing Gallery, Bridgeman Art Library

G

Machinery may make for efficiency and a standardization of life, but horse love is a bond of freemasonry which unites the entire race....
WILLIAM FAWCETT

G

THE RETURN HOME, *LUCY ELIZABETH KEMP WELCH*
(1869-1958), Private collection, Edimedia, Paris
Opposite: SUMMER EVENING AT KVITESEID
ERIK WERENSKIOLD (1855-1938)
National Gallery of Oslo, Bridgeman Art Library

H

A lovely horse is always an experience....It is an
emotional experience of the kind that is spoiled
by words.
BERYL MARKHAM

H

—————————

—————————

—————————

—————————

—————————

—————————

MAURER THE VET, *WILHELM LIEBL (1844-1900)*
Wallraf-Richartz-Museum, Köln, AKG-Berlin
Opposite: ANGLO-ARAB STALLION IN THE IMPERIAL
GARDENS OF VERSAILLES
THEODORE GERICAULT (1791-1824), *Edimedia, Paris*

I J

Horse, thou art truly a creature without equal, for thou fliest without wings and conquerest without sword.
THE KORAN

THE HUNT, *HENRI EMILIEU ROUSSEAU (1875-1933)*
Private collection, Edimedia, Paris
Opposite: HORSE-DRAWN CARRIAGE
MAX FELDBAUER (1869-1948)
Neue Meister Art Gallery, Dresden, AKG-Berlin

J

J

In riding a horse, we borrow freedom.
HELEN THOMSON, B.1943

K

THE END OF THE DAY, *ROBERT HOLLANDS WALKER*
Courtesy Angela Hone Watercolours, Marlow
Opposite: IN THE MOUNTAINS AT ALATAU
WASSILLI WASSILLEWITSCH WERESTSCHAGIN (1842-1904)
Private collection, AKG-Berlin

L

I will not change my horse with any that treads but on four pasterns.... When I bestride him, I soar, I am a hawk.
WILLIAM SHAKESPEARE (1564-1616)

L

LANDSCAPE NEAR HOME, *SEMJON AFANASSJEWITSCH*
(1902-1980), Neue Meister Art Gallery, Dresden
Opposite: THE RACECOURSE AT BOULOGNE SUR MER
THEO VAN RYSSELBERGHE (1862-1926)
Private collection, Edimedia, Paris

M

There is no secret so close as that between a rider and his horse.
ROBERT SMITH SURTEES (1803-1864)

M

FRIENDS
GEORGE ARMFIELD (FL. *1840-1884*)
Phillips, Son & Neale, London, Bridgeman Art Library
Opposite: ARAB HORSEMEN, *Y. GLACON*
Private collection, Edimedia, Paris

M

An extra pressure, a silent rebuke, an unseen praising, a firm correction: all these passed between us as through telegraph wires.
CHRISTILOT HANSON BOYLEN

FARMER PLOWING FIELD
GIOVANNI SEGANTINI (1858-1899)
Private collection, AKG-Berlin
Opposite: STABLE SCENE
CARL WILHELMSON, Private collection, Edimedia, Paris

DIE RECKEN
Victor Michailowitsch Wasnezow
Tret'jakov Gallery, Moscow
AKG-Berlin

O

The symbol of wide open spaces and freedom,
synonymous with nature in a mechanised world,
the horse ... feeds our imaginations.
BERTRAND LECLAIR

HORSEMEN IN BOULOGNE WOOD
Kees van Dongen (1877-1968)
Musée des Beaux-Arts, Le Havre, Giraudon/Bridgeman Art Library
Opposite: CROSSING THE FORD, *Paul Gauguin*
(1848-1903), Pushkin Museum, Moscow, AKG-Berlin

P

A horse is worth more than riches.
SPANISH PROVERB

P

AT THE BLACKSMITH'S FORGE
Thomas J. Purchas, Hampshire Gallery, AKG-Berlin
Opposite: HORSE SHOW
John Maggs (1819-1895)
Private collection, Edimedia, Paris

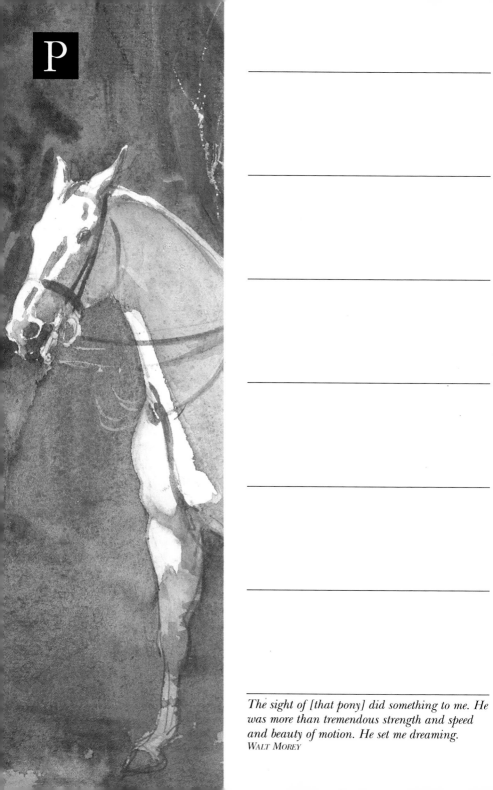

P

_____

_____

_____

_____

_____

_____

The sight of [that pony] did something to me. He
was more than tremendous strength and speed
and beauty of motion. He set me dreaming.
WALT MOREY

PQ

SHOWING AT TATTERSALLS, *ROBERT POLHILL BEVAN*
(1865-1925), *Private Collection, Bridgeman Art Library*
Opposite: GREY HORSE IN DAPPLED SUNLIGHT
SIR ALFRED MUNNINGS (1878-1959), *Bonhams, London*
The Sir Alfred Munnings Museum, Dedham, Bridgeman Art Library

R

_____

_____

_____

_____

_____

_____

Silence takes on a new quality when the only sound is that of regular and smooth hoof beats....
BERTRAND LECLAIR

R

————————————

————————————

————————————

————————————

————————————

————————————

INDIAN-PERSIAN MINIATURE,
17TH CENTURY, BATTLE SCENE
Philadelphia Free Library
AKG-Berlin

R

He trots the air, the earth sings when he touches it, the barest horn of his hoof is more musical than the pipe of Hermes.
WILLIAM SHAKESPEARE (1564-1616)

S

THE PRIDE OF PACHA, *ALFRED DE DREUX (1810-1860)*
Private collection, Edimedia, Paris
Opposite: DAPPLED HORSE
THEODORE GERICAULT (1791-1824)
Private collection, Edimedia, Paris

S

The eternal and wonderful sight of horses at liberty is magical to watch.
BERTRAND LECLAIR

S

THE TOWER OF THE BLUE HORSE
FRANZ MARC (1880-1916)
National Gallery, Berlin, AKG-Berlin
Opposite: BLUE HORSE, *FRANZ MARC (1880-1916)*
Galerie im Lenbachhaus, Munich, AKG-Berlin

S

Gipsy gold does not chink and glitter.
It gleams in the sun and neighs in the dark.
SAYING OF THE CLADDAGH GIPSIES OF GALWAY

S

GOING TO PASTURE
DOROTHY ADAMSON, D.1934
Towneley Hall Art Gallery & Museum, Burnley
Bridgeman Art Library

T

No one who longs for the "good old days" sighs
for the passing of the working horse. Not if he or
she loves horses.
MARION C. GARRETTY

T

HEAVY WORK
JULIUS PAUL JUNGHANS (1876-1953)
Ohne Kuenstlerrechte
AKG-Berlin

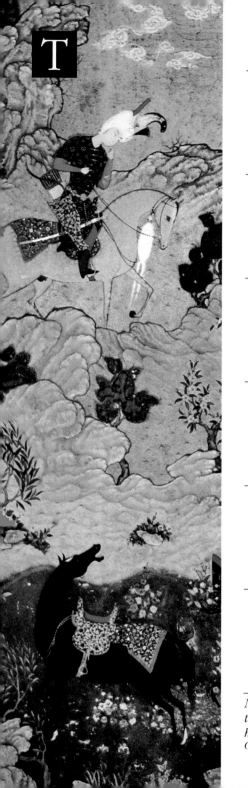

T

Many persons have sighed for the... "passing of the horse," but today, when only those who like horses own them, is a far better time for horses.
C.W. ANDERSON

T

INDIAN MINIATURE OF THE MOGUL PRINCE TALKING
TO DERVISHES, *Bodleian Library, Oxford,*
Philadelphia Free Library, AKG-Berlin
Opposite: PERSIAN BOOK PAINTING, 16TH CENTURY
British Museum, London, AKG-Berlin

U

Without the horse what would have become of man? It has served us for transport, in agriculture, industry since the dawn of time.
BERTRAND LECLAIR

U

ENTOURAGE OF THE THREE HOLY KINGS
BENOZZO GOZZOLI (1420-1497)
Palazzo Medici-Ricardi, Florence
AKG-Berlin

V

The air of heaven is that which blows between a horses's ears.
ARABIAN PROVERB

V

LE MARCHE
JULIUS VON BLASS (1845-1922)
Private collection, Edimedia, Paris
Opposite: THE HUNT, *GEORG HANS BUTTNER*
Private collection, Edimedia, Paris

W

_____

_____

_____

_____

_____

_____

*Closeness, friendship, affection: keeping your
own horse means all these things.*
BERTRAND LECLAIR

————————————

————————————

————————————

————————————

————————————

THE APPIAN WAY
HENRY HUBERT LA THANGUE
Oldham Art Gallery, Lancs, Bridgeman Art Library
Opposite: LABOUR, *HENNINGSEN (1850-1908)*
Private collection, Edimedia, Paris

W

_I am still under the impression there is nothing
alive quite so beautiful as a thoroughbred horse._
JOHN GALSWORTHY (1867-1933)

XYZ

MARE WITH FOALS
GEORGE STUBBS (1724-1806)
Private collection, AKG-Berlin